AVE MARIA

MUSIC BY GIULIO CACCINI
Arranged by Jonathan Wikeley

4

CACCINI'S *AVE MARIA* **IS AN EXQUISITE SETTING OF THE TRADITIONAL LATIN TEXT AND ITS BEAUTY AND SIMPLICITY HAS LED TO PERFORMANCES BY ANDREA BOCELLI, KATHERINE JENKINS, HAYLEY WESTENRA AND MANY OTHERS. HERE IT IS ARRANGED FOR TWO-PART CHOIRS AND PIANO ACCOMPANIMENT.**

ALSO AVAILABLE FROM MUSIC SALES:

BLACKBIRD (THE BEATLES)
SATB/PIANO – NO91300
SSA/PIANO – NO91289

FIELDS OF GOLD (STING)
SATB/PIANO – NOV940907
SSA/PIANO – NOV940918

HALLELUJAH (LEONARD COHEN, JEFF BUCKLEY AND OTHERS)
SATB/PIANO – NOV940863
SSA/PIANO – NOV940874

HERO (MARIAH CAREY, X FACTOR FINALISTS)
SATB/PIANO – NOV940830
SSA/PIANO – NOV940841

I HAVE A DREAM (ABBA)
SATB/PIANO – NOV170467
SSA/PIANO – NOV170478

KILLING ME SOFTLY WITH HIS SONG (ROBERTA FLACK, THE FUGEES)
SATB/PIANO – NOV170500
SSA/PIANO – NOV170522

MAN IN THE MIRROR (MICHAEL JACKSON)
SATB/PIANO NOV941281
SSA/PIANO NOV941094

OLIVER! CHORAL MEDLEY
SSA/PIANO – AM999086

REJOICE (KATHERINE JENKINS, IL DIVO)
SATB/PIANO – NOV940819

RUN (SNOW PATROL, LEONA LEWIS)
SATB/PIANO – NOV940852

RULE THE WORLD (TAKE THAT)
SATB/PIANO – NOV940940
SSA/PIANO – NOV940951

WONDERFUL TONIGHT (ERIC CLAPTON)
SATB/PIANO – NOV170489
SSA/PIANO – NOV170511

YOU RAISE ME UP (JOSH GROBAN, WESTLIFE AND OTHERS)
SATB/PIANO – NOV940929
SSA/PIANO – NOV940896

Novello Publishing Limited
part of The Music Sales Group
14-15 Berners Street
London W1T 3LJ, UK

Exclusive distributors:
Music Sales Limited
Newmarket Road
Bury St Edmunds
Suffolk IP33 3YB, UK

www.chesternovello.com

This publication © 2009
Novello & Company Limited

ISBN 978-1-84938-365-3

9 781849 383653